headwork reading

Madman's Corner

David Bennett

Oxford University Press

Madman's Corner

1
The Girl

There she was again. I had seen her in the same place for the last three Friday nights. Should I stop this time? No. I drove on. Who was she? Why was she always there?

I drive along the A162 every Friday night on my way home to Leeds. I am a plumber but I have not been working in Leeds for three months. I have been on a job in London. So every Friday night I have a 200-mile drive home. When I reach Madman's Corner I know I am 20 minutes from home.

'Next week,' I said to myself, 'next week if she is there I will stop.'

A week later I found myself driving towards Madman's Corner. It is a well-known bend in the area. A lot of cars have taken it too quickly. They have ended up in the muddy ditch at the side of the road. I slowed down and looked through the windscreen. Would she be there? My heart beat faster. At first I could not see anything. Then slowly, a figure came out of the darkness. There she was!

Four weeks in a row in the same spot at the same time. What was she doing?

I pulled the car over to the side of the road. I wound my window down.

'Where are you going?' I said.

'Leeds,' she replied.

'Get in then,' I said.

She picked up her bag and crash helmet. She opened the door and jumped into the back seat. At first I thought this a little funny. After all, the seat next to me was free. But then I was a man. She was a young woman. Better to be safe than sorry.

2
Helen

The next half an hour will stay with me for the rest of my life. She was called Helen. Helen Seddon. A pretty young thing. Long, straight brown hair and the most beautiful green eyes I had ever seen. But even those eyes were nothing compared to her smile. Her smile was ten times better. When she smiled her whole face lit up. That smile never left her face. It was as if she knew something that I did not.

It turned out that she only lived in the next street to me. I did not know her but then I was hardly ever at home. I had only moved in to my new house a few weeks ago.

15 Westover Street

Her address stuck in my mind. I would never forget it.

3
Steve

I got used to looking at her in my mirror. She could talk too! It was as if she was trying to tell me all about herself in just twenty minutes.

Helen was eighteen and at college. She was an only child. Her boyfriend was called Steve Lawton. He was a big motor bike fan and had his own Harley-Davidson. That would explain the crash helmet. She talked a lot about Steve. Strange though. She always talked about him as if he was far away.

We had been to the same school. I could not remember her. She was six years younger than me. We talked about the teachers. Old Mr Brown who could not keep us under control. Miss Carol who we called 'Christmas'. The Headmaster, Mr Naylor, whose wig fell off in assembly. She told me how she had always been in trouble at school. Once, she lit the gas tap in Science! She nearly set fire to the lab.

I liked her. She was exciting and full of fun. I nearly asked her why she stood at Madman's Corner every Friday. I wish I had. It would have helped me get over what happened.

4
She's Gone!

Helen was in the middle of telling me about her parents when she stopped. I looked in the mirror but could not see her. I moved the mirror about so that I could see the whole of the back seat. There was no sign of her. I slammed on the brakes. The car skidded to a halt and I jumped out. I grabbed the back door handle and pulled it hard. The door opened and the light came on. The back seat looked empty at first. No Helen. No bag. But there was the crash helmet. A black crash helmet with a cracked visor.

I ran back down the road looking from side to side. There was no sign of her. She had vanished. All that was left was the crash helmet. I walked slowly back to the car trying to clear my head. What should I do? I picked up the crash helmet and turned it over. Inside it said:

Helen Seddon
15 Westover Street
Beeston
Leeds

That was all that was left. Just an address.

There was only one thing I could do. Drive to Westover Street and tell her parents what had happened. It would sound stupid I know but I had to tell them. Tell them what? I picked up their daughter but she had vanished? What would they think of me?

5
Helen's House

I started to drive and five minutes later I was outside her house. A man opened the door. He looked old. His hair was white. His face was full of pain. His eyes sad. He said nothing. If this was her father then he was a lot older than she had described him.

I explained to him what had happened. Where I had picked her up. How I had seen her in the same spot for the last four weeks.

What she had told me of her life. He listened
without saying anything.

When I had finished he said, 'Come in.'

He led me into the front room. On the wall was a large photo of Helen. 'Is that who you picked up?' he said.

He knew it was.

'Yes, that is her,' I said.

'Two years ago she was on the back of Steve's bike. They were hit by a drunk driver doing sixty going round Madman's Corner. He killed the pair of them. Murdered is a better word.'

What could I say?

He carried on, 'I am not surprised to see you.'

'Why not?' I replied.

'You are the third person to come and tell me the same story in the last four weeks.'

I stood with my mouth open. A Ghost? I had given a lift to a ghost?

I walked slowly back to my car. On the back seat was her crash helmet. I picked it up. It was hard and smooth. At least it was real. Inside it said:

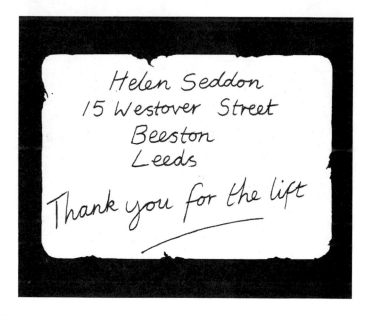

Helen Seddon
15 Westover Street
Beeston
Leeds

Thank you for the lift

Oxford University Press, Great Clarendon Street,
Oxford, OX2 6DP

Oxford   New York
Athens   Auckland   Bangkok   Bogota   Bombay
Buenos Aires   Calcutta   Cape Town   Dar es Salaam
Delhi   Florence   Hong Kong   Istanbul   Karachi
Kuala Lumpur   Madras   Madrid   Melbourne
Mexico City   Nairobi   Paris   Singapore
Taipei   Tokyo   Toronto

and associated companies in
Berlin   Ibadan

Oxford is a trade mark of Oxford University Press

Printed in Great Britain

Illustrations by Jackie McQuade